Punctuation Matters
Book 3

G000298753

It is intended that this book should be used to reinforce key skills as recommended in the English National Curriculum at Key Stages 2 & 3 and in the National Literacy Strategy.

CONTENTS

by Hilda King

Hilda King Educational, Ashwells Manor Drive, Penn, Buckinghamshire HP10 8EU

Typeset by: Penn Secretarial Services
Illustrations by: Brian Watson
Printed by: Watkiss Studios

First Published 1998
Reprinted and revised 1999
Reprinted 2001
Reprinted 2002

ISBN 1 873533 53 5

Speech marks

Speech marks are also called inverted commas or quotation marks.

They are used before and after **spoken words**.

Speech marks may be single ‘ ’ or double “ ”.

Double ones are used throughout this book.

Remember the comma: it is used after: He said, She asked, etc.

Look at the example: He said, “We have lost the cat.”

Remember this order:

1. a comma   ,

2. opening speech marks   “

3. a capital letter   A

4. a full stop   .

5. closing speech marks   ”

e.g. John said, “That was a good match.”

Remember: Closing speech marks always go **after** the full stop.

Add the commas, speech marks and full stops.

1. She said It is four o'clock

2. You said It isn't true

3. Pierre said I'll wait

4. She said Yes please

5. The teacher said Write this

6. They said That's rubbish

7. Mum said I want a cup of tea

8. He said It's cool

9. I said No, thank you

10. Dad said Mum needs you

11. We said We love peppermints

12. I said It is funny

Speech marks

Add commas, speech marks, capital letters and full stops to each sentence below.

1.   he said she can use the computer

....

2.   the teacher said you have done very well

....

3.   james said i want to watch the football

....

4.   asim said let's buy a curry

....

5.   amy said please come to my party

....

6.   she said i am going shopping now

....

7.   they said send her some flowers

....

8.   mum said please let the dog in

....

9.   laura said my shoes are too small

....

10. the postman said that parcel is very heavy

....

Speech marks

> **Remember:**
> the spoken words can also come at the
> beginning of a sentence.
>
> **Rule:**
> when spoken words come first, always put a *comma*
> before the closing speech marks, *never* a full stop.
>
> e.g. "I arrest you," said the policeman.

Rewrite the following examples. Put in <u>all</u> the punctuation marks.

1. we are afraid of spiders said the twins

....

2. the film is just starting said the child

....

3. you are always talking on the telephone said mum

....

4. the train will leave at ten o'clock said the announcer

....

5. my soup is cold the man said to the waiter

....

6. remember to shut the gate said the farmer

....

7. take three tablets a day said the doctor

....

8. i have caught lots of fish today said the happy fisherman

....

9. i want to take a photograph of the waterfall said peter

....

Speech marks

Remember:
the spoken words of a sentence are sometimes *interrupted* by the speaker.
Rule: *never* use a capital letter (except for I or proper names) to begin the second part of the interrupted speech.

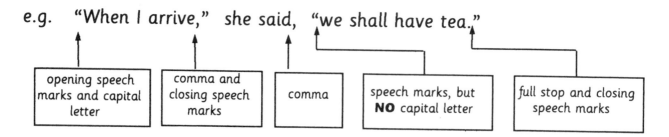

e.g. "When I arrive," she said, "we shall have tea."

| opening speech marks and capital letter | comma and closing speech marks | comma | speech marks, but **NO** capital letter | full stop and closing speech marks |

Rewrite the following sentences. Put in *all* the punctuation marks and capital letters.

1. it is half-past two she said so its time to go

....

2. athletics is good fun he said but I prefer to play football

....

3. if you come to stay he said you can sleep in the top bunk

....

4. when you are sitting still the teacher said i will read the story

....

5. theres a lorry said the little boy and it has red wheels

....

6. dont go swimming now mum said because its dinner time

....

7. i can do the crossword she said even though the clues are difficult

....

8. you cant go that way said the policeman because the road is blocked

....

9. if we miss that bus said sophie we shall be late for school

....

Speech marks

Rewrite the following sentences. Add *all* the punctuation marks and capital letters.

1. she smiled and said i hope you enjoyed your ice cream

    ....

2. grandma said im nearly eighty

    ....

3. i love watching cricket matches said jonathan

    ....

4. the florist said i shall give you six red roses

    ....

5. the coat suits you said the assistant and its in the sale

    ....

6. ive just had a haircut said rapunzel to the prince so youd better
    buy a ladder

    ....

    ....

7. i love pork chops said the wolf to the three little pigs

    ....

8. if there are no batteries said john the torch wont work

    ....

9. long john silver said this parrot has sharp claws

    ....

10. the tyre is flat said the mechanic because there is a nail in it

    ....

11. amanda said i love chocolate

    ....

12 dry the glasses carefully said mum or you might break one

    ....

Speech marks

> **Remember:**
> spoken words sometimes end with a question mark
> or an exclamation mark.
> The question mark or exclamation mark always
> comes *before* the closing speech marks.
>
> e.g.   "What time is it?" he asked.
> "Help!" she cried, "I'm falling!"

**Rewrite the following sentences. Add *all* the punctuation marks
and capital letters.**

1.   can I go too she asked ....

2.   goodness he exclaimed ....

3.   where am I asked the man ....

4.   where is my rabbit said the boy ....

5.   quick said nasir ....

6.   come in said jane ....

7.   i hate exams cried paul ....

8.   leave me alone screamed deena

....

9.   stop said the team manager

....

10. does your head go to the top of your hat said the little boy to
the policeman

....

....

11. will the new bridge take all the heavy lorries asked the man

....

12. if you go to the fair will you buy me some popcorn she asked

....

Speech marks

Add speech marks, commas, question marks, exclamation marks, and full stops to the sentences.

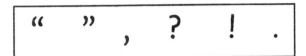

1. Goodness I'm sorry I am late said the busy dentist

2. I have done my homework quickly What shall I do now she asked

3. The teacher said Don't do that Harry Sandra is crying now

4. Sit down I must take your temperature said the nurse

5. Tidy up your room It's in a terrible mess said my mum

6. How silly I am I've put on your coat by mistake said Emma

Add the speech marks to the following.

1. Ouch! he said. You have run over my foot.

2. That was a good dive, said the swimming instructor. Do you want to go off the top board now?

3. Who? asked my sister. Are you sure it's Billy?

4. Look at the sky! said Mark. Those are not stars. They're fireworks.

5. I'm going to Blackpool, said Ranjit. Where are you going?

6. How long has the drain been blocked? asked the plumber. It's probably full of leaves.

Speech marks

> **Remember:**
> **you do not always have to use the verb _to say_.**
> **You can use other verbs:**
> e.g. to announce, to remark, to continue, to explain.

Here are more verbs:

to ask	to shout	to think	to mutter
to reply	to whisper	to yell	to cry

Rewrite the following examples, putting in the capital letters, the speech marks and all other punctuation.

1. it was a sad day for me remarked the old engine driver when the last steam train ran ....

    ....

2. the play starts at eight o clock replied the theatre manager

    ....

3. by the way she continued i shant be going to the match this saturday

    ....

4. as he walked along john muttered to himself i wish i hadnt spent all my pocket money ....

    ....

5. this is the best way to solve the problem the teacher explained

    ....

6. the organiser announced the fathers race will start in five minutes

    ....

7. victoria whispered to her best friend please sit next to me at the tea party ....

    ....

8. i am not quite sure of the directions nicola thought but i am sure i must turn right ....

    ....

Speech marks

Remember:
start a new line every time the speaker changes.
e.g.   "Hello," said John.
  "Hello," said Lucy. "How are you feeling today?"

Rewrite the following sentences, starting a new line where necessary. Always indent a new line with a new speaker: to indent means to leave a space (about 1cm) between the margin of the paper and the first word.

Add the speech marks and the correct punctuation.

1. How can I help you asked the doctor I've got a pain in my back said Ben

....

....

2. You are clear to land said the controller Thank you replied the pilot

....

....

3. Why are you shouting asked dad You've shut my finger in the car door screamed mum

....

....

4. Halt said the watchman Who goes there

....

5. You have won first prize the judge said Thank you said Mrs Button.

....

....

Rewrite the story below on a separate sheet of paper. Put in the speech marks, start a new line when needed, remember to indent it.

It's no good. I can't do my homework, said Josie. Why? said her mother. You always like doing maths. I just don't understand it. What am I going to do? sobbed Josie. Let me see. Look! It's not page nine you should be doing, it's page eight. No wonder you can't do it! You're looking at the wrong page, laughed Josie's mother.

11

Speech marks

Revision page

Rewrite the following story on a separate sheet of paper putting in the capital letters, speech marks and all other punctuation.

come quickly mum shouted sarah

whatever is the matter dear asked her mother as she ran into the garden

both the guinea pigs have escaped cried the little girl

how on earth did that happen said mum we are always so careful to shut the door of the hutch

its my fault sobbed sarah because i didnt close it properly

dont waste time crying exclaimed her mother lets look for them

they searched the vegetable garden and the flower beds and the field where their old donkey grazed but all in vain

sarah was very unhappy i shall never see my lovely guinea pigs again she wept

at school next day she kept saying to herself why was I so careless why didnt i shut the door properly

she need not have worried when she came home from school her mother greeted her with a big smile

ive just found the guinea pigs she said they are hiding in the old fox hole at the end of the field dad is coming home this minute to help catch them she added

thank goodness shrieked sarah what a relief

the guinea pigs were soon back in their cosy hutch

ill always look after them from now on promised sarah

Write a title for the story.

Indirect or reported speech

> **Remember:**
> indirect speech is a report of what has been said.
> It does not need speech marks.

Look at the following examples. Can you spot the differences between direct and indirect speech?

e.g. 1. "**I am going** to the cinema," said James. (Direct speech)

James said that **he was going** to the cinema. (Indirect speech)

2. "**Tom will play** tennis tomorrow," said Ann. (Direct speech)

Ann said that **Tom would play** tennis tomorrow. (Indirect speech)

> **Rules:** when direct speech becomes indirect speech,
>   a) there are no speech marks
>   b) the verb sometimes changes tense
>   c) the person sometimes changes.
>
> **e.g.**   "**I am** sorry," said Paul. (Direct speech)
>   Paul said that **he was** sorry. (Indirect speech)
>
> **Note:**   a) no speech marks
>   b) **am** becomes **was**
>   c) **I** becomes **he**

Change the following examples into indirect speech.

1. "You must not park there," said the policeman.

....

2. "I have seen that video," said the little boy.

....

3. The window cleaner said, "Those windows are very dirty."

....

4. "I think that dog will bite me," said the paperboy.

....

5. "I hope she will reach the summit," said the climbing instructor.

....

13

Indirect or reported speech

> **Here is an example of how indirect speech
> has been changed to direct speech.
> Dad said that he could cook twenty hot dogs at once.
> Dad said, "*I can cook* twenty hot dogs at once."**

Note: As with direct speech you can use other words instead of
said, e.g. cried, answered, whispered, shouted, warned.

**Change the following examples from indirect speech to direct
speech.**

1. The little girl shouted that she could swim forty lengths.

....

2. The queen whispered that her tiara was too big.

....

3. The weather man warned that it would snow tonight.

....

4. Alice moaned that she had twisted her ankle.

....

5. The journalist reported that there had been a hurricane in Florida.

....

**Change the following examples from direct to indirect speech or
from indirect to direct speech.**

1. The teacher admitted that she had lost the book.

....

2. "Those eggs are broken," said the check-out girl.

....

3. Snow White declared that she did not like apples.

....

4. "We like going to the Science Museum," agreed the children.

....

Indirect or reported speech
Indirect questions

> **An indirect question reports that a question has been asked.**
> **It does not need a question mark.**

Here is an example of how a **direct** question has been changed to an **indirect** question: "Where have I put the teapot?" asked Grandma.

Grandma asked where she had put the teapot.

Remember:

a) there are no speech marks

b) the person may change

c) the tense of the verb may change

d) there are no question marks.

Change the following direct questions into indirect questions.

1.　"Where am I?" asked Sleeping Beauty.

....

2.　"Why is the door unlocked?" enquired the puzzled detective.

....

3.　"Can you see the water in the well?" I asked the surveyor.

....

4.　"How many stars can you see?" the astronomer asked the children.

....

Here is an example of how an **indirect** question has been changed to a **direct** question:　My friend asked me if my cocoa was too hot to drink.

"Is your cocoa too hot to drink?" asked my friend.

Remember:

a) you need speech marks

b) the tense of the verb may change

c) the person may change

d) you need question marks.

Change the following indirect questions into direct questions.

1.　I asked the photographer when the proofs would be ready.

....

2.　Sherlock Holmes asked Doctor Watson if he wanted to study the case.

....

3.　The chef asked when the potatoes would be ready.

....

4.　The bus driver asked if I wanted to get off at the next stop.

....

The colon

:

:

> A colon has three main uses.
> It is often used to introduce a list.
> e.g. I love sweets: mints, jellybabies and toffees.

Add the colons to the examples below.

1. When I go camping I need all these things a sleeping bag, a torch, a pan and some matches.

2. I like bright colours red, orange, yellow and green.

3. Mrs Blob bought lots of fruit apples, pears and bananas.

4. I like everything about the seaside the sea, the sand and the candyfloss.

5. My new mountain bicycle has everything wide wheels, twenty-five gears and a racing saddle.

Rearrange the words, add the colons and the commas, where needed, in the examples below.

1. six week The days a postman mail delivers Tuesday Friday Wednesday Monday Thursday Saturday

....

....

2. traffic change lights Watch the amber to red green to

....

3. order the The in are colours rainbow of this   green blue red violet yellow indigo orange

....

....

4. the year order Put the into seasons right the of   autumn spring winter summer.

....

The colon

A colon is used to *introduce* an *explanation* or *reference* to the first part of a sentence.
e.g. He told me his problem: he is very lonely.

Add the colons to the examples below.

1. The audience left the theatre the fire bell had rung.

2. That maths exercise is difficult I do not understand algebra.

3. As soon as the director heard her sing he knew here was a star.

4. Tom was glad his shorts were red and white his favourite colours.

5. I am going to the cinema there is a film I really want to see.

6. The book I am reading is exciting I want to finish it.

7. The plant has died mum forgot to water it.

Rearrange the words, adding the colons and full stops in the following sentences.

1. cannot ski We raining snow there and is it no is

   ....

2. library I to went the   wanted science I book a

   ....

3. frightened dog was The   firework made bang loud a had the

   ....

4. lotion We suntan need use to   today hot the very is sun

   ....

5. to We stand had   was the full train very

   ....

6. ice the Don't cake   soft is too the icing

   ....

17

The colon

> **A colon is used to _introduce_ a quotation,
> a saying or a famous speech.**
>
> **e.g. The proverb says: too many cooks spoil the broth.**
> **Note: do not put speech marks round proverbs or sayings.**

Add the colons to the examples below.

1. Richard III said "A horse, a horse, my kingdom for a horse."

2. There is an old saying you can't teach an old dog new tricks.

3. The first line of Wordsworth's Daffodils is "I wandered lonely as a cloud."

4. Before the Battle of Trafalgar in 1805, Lord Nelson said "England expects every man will do his duty."

5. The little boy fell off his bicycle more haste less speed.

Rewrite the following sentences. Add the colons and speech marks where necessary.

1. Do not worry every cloud has a silver lining.

   ....

2. Juliet asked O Romeo, Romeo! Wherefore art thou Romeo?

   ....

3. My dad arrived late better late than never.

   ....

4. Martin Luther King once said I have a dream.

   ....

5. Do it now a stitch in time saves nine.

   ....

6. Winston Churchill said I have nothing to offer but blood, toil, sweat and tears.

   ....

   ....

The semicolon

;	;

> **A semicolon makes a shorter pause than a full stop.**

It is often used instead of a full stop to join ideas more closely together in one sentence rather than two sentences.

e.g.   It was dark and cold; it was raining

Add semicolons to the examples below.

1. The sea was rough the waves crashed on to the rocks.

2. The oranges were easy to peel they were very sweet and juicy.

3. Jane loved the book she read three more chapters.

4. The chairs were put away the table was cleared.

5. The cargo was loaded the passengers were seated.

6. He climbed five flights of stairs two more and he would be there.

Add the semicolons and *all other* punctuation to the sentences below.

1. the baby was crying she was unhappy in her cot

....

2. the ring sparkled the diamonds flashed

....

3. no man is an island everyone needs a friend

....

4. we have to go the taxi is waiting

....

5. a wise man is often silent a fool often talks too much

....

6. it was a clear cloudless night the stars shone brightly

....

The semicolon

A semicolon can be used instead of joining words,
e.g. but, and, because or since.
e.g. He wanted to come home but I told him to stay away.
He wanted to come home; I told him to stay away.

Rewrite the following examples putting a semicolon instead of a joining word.

1.   The old lady was shivering because her coat was too thin.

   ....

2.   He began the book but he didn't finish it.

   ....

3.   I am going to see my friend and I will take her Christmas present with me.

   ....

4.   I do not trust him since he lied to me.

   ....

5.   He has left already so I will not see him.

   ....

Now rewrite the following examples putting in a joining word instead of a semicolon. Use each of the following joining words once: but, because, since, and, so.

1.   My dog is fat; he eats too much.

   ....

2.   The iron was too hot; I ruined my skirt.

   ....

3.   I went to the library; I used the reference books.

   ....

4.   He sent her a message; she cannot meet him.

   ....

5.   It was difficult to read; one of the light bulbs was missing.

   ....

Paragraphs

> **Paragraphs make a piece of writing easier to read and understand**

Paragraphs can consist of one, two or more sentences and can be of any length.

Sentences are grouped together in one paragraph because they are about one particular idea or topic.

Note: a)   always begin a paragraph on a new line

            b)* always indent the first line of a paragraph.
(to indent means to leave a space of about 1cm between the margin of the paper and the first word.)

Look at the following box containing two paragraphs.

> The year is divided into four seasons. They are called spring, summer, autumn and winter. People often have a favourite season, but each one has its own attractions.
>
>   I like spring because the days are getting longer and warmer and I can play outside. Easter falls in the spring and I have a holiday from school.

The first paragraph is about the year and its seasons. The second paragraph is about one season, the spring.

Now develop the theme of the seasons by copying out these two paragraphs on a separate sheet of paper and adding three short paragraphs of your own about summer, autumn and winter.

When you have completed this work, you will have written five paragraphs. Make sure that each new paragraph begins on a new line and is indented.

---

* *It is becoming more common to leave a double space between paragraphs and not to indent. Indenting, however, helps the children to understand the significance of paragraphs and it is recommended at this stage.*

Paragraphs

Read the story below. It is divided into two paragraphs.

Katy's House

Nine-year-old Katy lives in a large old farmhouse with her mother and father and her two older sisters. The front part of their house was built in 1765 during the reign of King George III. The back part was added in Victorian times.

When Katy moved there from London, the house had been empty for several years. Central heating, a new bathroom and a new kitchen all had to be fitted to make the family comfortable. The old electric wiring had to be replaced because it was dangerous.

Read the rest of the story. Rewrite it on a separate sheet of paper, dividing it into three paragraphs. Remember to look for a particular idea or topic that will connect the sentences in each paragraph. Always begin a paragraph on a new line and indent the first line of a new paragraph.

The three children love the large old house with its two staircases. There are five bedrooms. This means that Katy and her sisters can each have their own bedroom. Outside there are two barns; the small one has been made into a den for the girls. On a wet day they and their friends can play music as loudly as they like without disturbing anyone. Now the girls live in the country they are a long way from their school. The school bus stops outside the farmhouse. They enjoy the journey with their friends.

Now, on a separate sheet of paper, write four paragraphs of your own on: **Why we need to save our trees, A day in the country** or another topic that you would like to write about.

Paragraphs

**How to paragraph a story and
put the events in the right sequence.**

**Rule:
a story always has a beginning,
a middle and an end.**

A beginning: the first paragraph is the introductory paragraph, because it introduces the reader to the main character or the main idea.

A middle: the second and following paragraphs tell more about the subject matter. There can be as many paragraphs in the middle as the theme requires.

An end: the final paragraph brings the story to a conclusion. It sums up the story.

Below are the first words of five paragraphs of a story about a day at the seaside.

On a separate sheet of paper expand each group of words into a short paragraph, remembering the rule about a beginning, a middle and an end. Rearrange the order of the paragraphs in the correct sequence.

A Day at the Seaside

1. The children loved playing in the rock pools ....

2. It was a hot Saturday in August when dad said, "Let's go to the seaside tomorrow." So ....

3. On the journey home ....

4. When it started to rain ....

5. Suddenly they had their first glimpse of the sea as ....

Letter writing

There are two main types of letter: personal and business

A personal letter is usually informal and is written to a relation, a friend or a neighbour. An example of the outline of a personal letter is set out below on the right. In this example the address is indented and commas are included. This is normal for a handwritten personal letter.

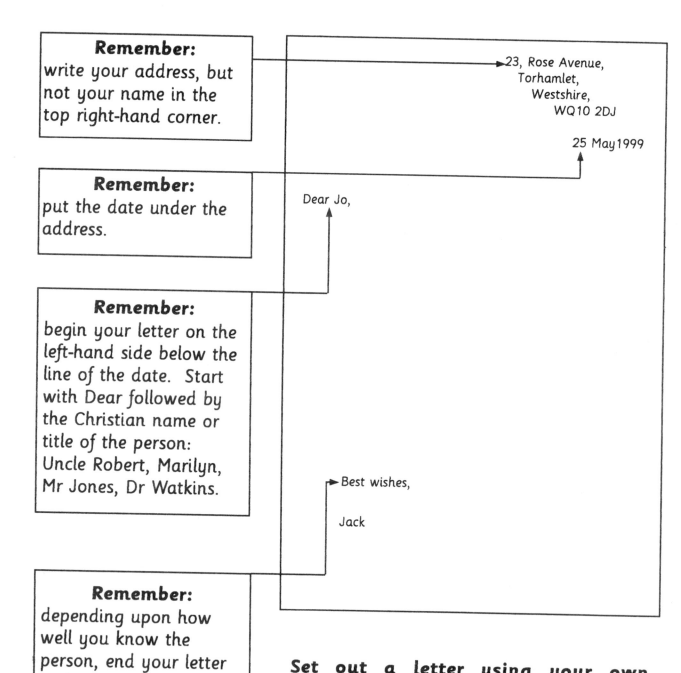

Remember: write your address, but not your name in the top right-hand corner.

23, Rose Avenue,
Torhamlet,
Westshire,
WQ10 2DJ

25 May 1999

Remember: put the date under the address.

Dear Jo,

Remember: begin your letter on the left-hand side below the line of the date. Start with Dear followed by the Christian name or title of the person: Uncle Robert, Marilyn, Mr Jones, Dr Watkins.

Best wishes,

Jack

Remember: depending upon how well you know the person, end your letter with: Love, Best wishes, Yours sincerely,.

Set out a letter using your own address and today's date. Do not write a complete letter. Simply put the outline as in the example above.

24

Letter writing

It is easier to read a letter, whether personal or business, if it is set out correctly in paragraphs.

Look at the following examples of a personal letter. The first example shows you how *not* to set it out.

Cub Camp Peg Lane Tentingham TZ3 6RB 4th July 1998. Dear Mum, I am having a really good time. We have had beans and porridge every day and lots of tomato sauce. Mr Bramley is feeling better now. The doctor took the tent peg out of his foot and he only had to have ten stitches. It has rained every day and all my clothes are wet. On Tuesday we went to a museum, which was boring. We had a packed lunch with cucumber sandwiches which I did not like. Will you be picking me up on Saturday? I hope you will. Love Michael.

The second example shows you how to set it out *correctly* in four paragraphs.

Cub Camp,
Peg Lane,
Tentingham,
TZ3 6RB

4th July 1999

Dear Mum,

I am having a really good time. We have had beans and porridge every day and lots of tomato sauce.

Mr Bramley is feeling better now. The doctor took the tent peg out of his foot and he only had to have ten stitches.

It has rained every day and all my clothes are wet. On Tuesday we went to a museum, which was boring. We had a packed lunch with cucumber sandwiches which I did not like.

Will you be picking me up on Saturday? I hope you will.

Love,
Michael.

Write two personal letters using the correct layout and punctuation.

a. You have chickenpox. Write a letter to your friend.
b. You are living in Australia for six months. Write a letter to your cousin telling him what it is like there.

Letter writing
Personal letters

There are many different ways of ending a personal letter. In addition to Love, Best wishes or Yours sincerely, you can write Yours, Yours truly, With much love, All my love, Lots of love, Your friend, Your loving nephew/niece, Your loving son/daughter and many more depending upon how well you know the person to whom you are writing the letter.

Now write a letter to your best friend explaining why you are in hospital. Choose your own reason. Here are some suggestions:

   a)   **you broke your leg playing football**
   b)   **you had your appendix removed**
   c)   **you fell downstairs and broke your collarbone.**

Remember:

to follow all the rules for letter writing, putting your own address at the top and today's date. Divide your letter into three paragraphs.

Below are the words of a thank you letter to Aunty Alice. Rewrite it on a separate sheet of paper, putting your own address at the top and today's date. Set it out correctly in four paragraphs.

Dear Aunty Alice, Thank you very much for my birthday presents. The money will be very useful because I am saving up for a new computer game. Thank you for the garden gnome, too. That was a very unusual present. I do hope that Uncle Fred is feeling better. I was so sorry to hear that he had fallen off his bicycle. I had a lovely birthday. All my friends came to see me and we watched videos and played some tapes. I hope to see you both soon. Love from Judith.

Letter writing
Business letters

Business letters are formal letters. There are many types: to a bank manager, a shop or garage manager, a headteacher, a local councillor, a Member of Parliament, or a personnel director.

Below is an example of how to set out a business letter. When writing business letters it is becoming more common not to use indents and commas in either addresses or after Dear Mr ... and Yours sincerely.

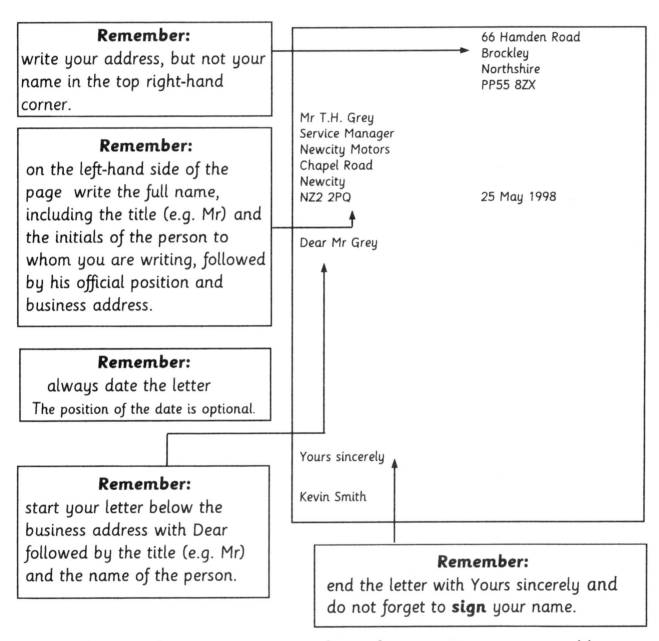

Remember:
write your address, but not your name in the top right-hand corner.

Remember:
on the left-hand side of the page write the full name, including the title (e.g. Mr) and the initials of the person to whom you are writing, followed by his official position and business address.

Remember:
always date the letter
The position of the date is optional.

Remember:
start your letter below the business address with Dear followed by the title (e.g. Mr) and the name of the person.

Remember:
end the letter with Yours sincerely and do not forget to **sign** your name.

66 Hamden Road
Brockley
Northshire
PP55 8ZX

Mr T.H. Grey
Service Manager
Newcity Motors
Chapel Road
Newcity
NZ2 2PQ   25 May 1998

Dear Mr Grey

Yours sincerely

Kevin Smith

Set out a business letter on a separate sheet of paper. Put your own address at the top and today's date. Write to Mr B. D. Jones, Personnel Director, The Glove Company, Toptown, Topshire, TX9 8EG.

Do not write a complete letter. Simply put the outline as in the example above.

Letter writing
Business letters

Sometimes you will have to write a business letter without knowing the name of the person to whom you are sending it.

e.g. You need to write to your bank manager and you do not know his name. Begin your letter with Dear Sir. Study the example below.

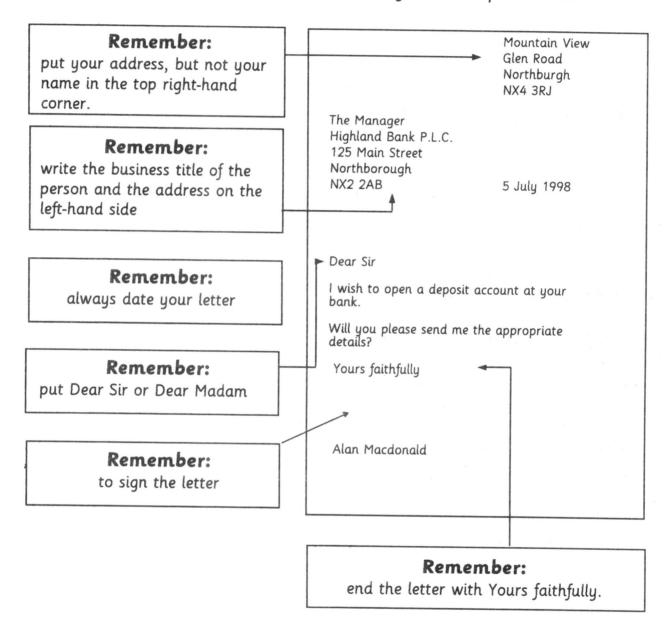

Remember:
put your address, but not your name in the top right-hand corner.

Remember:
write the business title of the person and the address on the left-hand side

Remember:
always date your letter

Remember:
put Dear Sir or Dear Madam

Remember:
to sign the letter

Mountain View
Glen Road
Northburgh
NX4 3RJ

The Manager
Highland Bank P.L.C.
125 Main Street
Northborough
NX2 2AB   5 July 1998

Dear Sir

I wish to open a deposit account at your bank.

Will you please send me the appropriate details?

   Yours faithfully

Alan Macdonald

Remember:
end the letter with Yours faithfully.

Note: If you start a business letter with Dear Sir or Madam, end it with Yours faithfully. If you start a business letter with Dear Mr Jones end it with Yours sincerely.

Write a short letter of two paragraphs to the Manager of the Central Bank, 25 West Street, Oldbridge, Eastshire, OG4 9AH asking for details of a savings account you wish to open for yourself. You do not know the Manager's name.

28

Letter writing
How to address an envelope

1. Do not start the address too high. Allow space for the stamp and the postmark. Start about halfway down the envelope.

2. Always write clearly.

3. Make sure the address is as complete as possible, including the name of the person; number or name of house; name of road, street, avenue,etc.; name of town. If it is a large city or town you can leave out the county. If it is a smaller town or a village, put in the county before the postcode. Always include the postcode if you know it.

Below are two examples of addresses for personal letters:

Envelope A

Miss Tracy Brown,
33, Hawthorn Avenue,
Northside,
Midcity, MX9 5PC

Envelope B

Mr & Mrs F.J. Green
The Laurels
Church Lane
Anyvillage
Anyshire AX21 2BD

The address on an envelope for a personal letter can be indented and commas used as shown on envelope A. The address on envelope B is not indented and commas are omitted. Addresses on business envelopes, which are usually typed, are set out as shown on envelope B.

In each case, the Post Office prefers postal codes not to be followed by a full stop.

Answer page

N.B. (i) Capital letters for 'mum' and 'dad' are optional but lower case is used in this book.
(ii) Some of the easier examples are not covered in the answer pages.

Page 3

1. She said, "It is four o'clock." 2. You said, "It isn't true." 3. Pierre said, "I'll wait." 4 She said, "Yes, please." 5. The teacher said, "Write this." 6. They said, "That's rubbish." 7. Mum said, "I want a cup of tea." 8. He said, "It's cool." 9. I said, "No, thank you." 10. Dad said, "Mum needs you." 11. We said, "We love peppermints." 12. I said, "It is funny."

Page 4

1. He said, "She can use the computer." 2. The teacher said, "You have done very well." 3. James said, "I want to watch the football." 4. Asim said, "Let's buy a curry." 5. Amy said, "Please come to my party." 6. She said, "I am going shopping now." 7. They said, "Send her some flowers." 8. Mum said, "Please let the dog in." 9. Laura said, "My shoes are too small." 10. The postman said, "That parcel is very heavy."

Page 5

1. "We are afraid of spiders," said the twins. 2. "The film is just starting," said the child. 3. "You are always talking on the telephone," said mum. 4. "The train will leave at ten o'clock," said the announcer. 5. "My soup is cold," the man said to the waiter. 6. "Remember to shut the gate," said the farmer. 7. "Take three tablets a day," said the doctor. 8. "I have caught lots of fish today," said the happy fisherman. 9. "I want to take a photograph of the waterfall," said Peter.

Page 6

1. "It is half past two," she said, "so it's time to go." 2. "Athletics is good fun," he said, "but I prefer to play football." 3. "If you come to stay," he said, "you can sleep in the top bunk." 4. "When you are sitting still," the teacher said, "I will read the story." 5. "There's a lorry," said the little boy, "and it has red wheels." 6. "Don't go swimming now," mum said, "because it's dinner time." 7. "I can do the crossword," she said, "even though the clues are difficult." 8. "You can't go that way," said the policeman, "because the road is blocked." 9. "If we miss that bus," said Sophie, "we shall be late for school."

Page 7

1. She smiled and said, "I hope you enjoyed your ice cream." 2. Grandma said, "I'm nearly eighty." 3. "I love watching cricket matches," said Jonathan. 4. The florist said, "I shall give you six red roses." 5. "The coat suits you," said the assistant, "and it's in the sale." 6. "I've just had a hair cut," said Rapunzel to the prince, "so you'd better buy a ladder." 7. "I love pork chops," said the wolf to the three little pigs. 8. "If there are no batteries," said John, "the torch won't work." 9. Long John Silver said, "This parrot has sharp claws." 10. "The tyre is flat," said the mechanic, "because there is a nail in it." 11. Amanda said, "I love chocolate." 12. "Dry the glasses carefully," said mum, "or you might break one."

Page 8

1. "Can I go too?" she asked. 2."Goodness!" he exclaimed. 3. "Where am I?" asked the man. 4. "Where is my rabbit?" said the boy. 5. "Quick!" said Nasir. 6. "Come in," said Jane. 7. "I hate exams!" cried Paul. 8. "Leave me alone!" screamed Deena. 9. "Stop!" said the team manager. 10. "Does your head go to the top of your hat?" said the little boy to the policeman. 11. "Will the new bridge take all the heavy lorries?" asked the man. 12. "If you go to the fair will you buy me some popcorn?" she asked.

Page 9 (top)

1. "Goodness! I'm sorry I am late," said the busy dentist. 2. "I have done my homework quickly. What shall I do now?" she asked. 3. The teacher said, "Don't do that, Harry. Sandra is crying now." 4. "Sit down. I must take your temperature," said the nurse. 5. "Tidy up your room. It's in a terrible mess," said my mum. 6. "How silly I am! I've put on your coat by mistake," said Emma.

Page 9 (bottom)

1. "Ouch!" he said. "You have run over my foot." 2. "That was a good dive," said the swimming instructor. "Do you want to go off the top board now?" 3. "Who?" asked my sister. "Are you sure it's Billy?" 4. "Look at the sky!" said Mark. "Those are not stars. They are fireworks." 5. "I'm going to Blackpool" said Ranjit. "Where are you going?" 6. "How long has the drain been blocked?" asked the plumber. "It's probably full of leaves."

Page 10

1. "It was a sad day for me," remarked the old engine driver, "when the last steam train ran." 2. "The play starts at eight o'clock," replied the theatre manager. 3. "By the way," she continued, "I shan't be going to the match this Saturday." 4. As he walked along, John muttered to himself, "I wish I hadn't spent all my pocket money." 5. "This is the best way to solve the problem," the teacher explained. 6. The organiser announced, "The fathers' race will start in five minutes." 7. Victoria whispered to her best friend, "Please sit next to me at the tea party." 8. "I am not quite sure of the directions," Nicola thought, "but I am sure I must turn right."

Answer page (cont.)

Page 11 (top)

1. "How can I help you?" asked the doctor.
   "I've got a pain in my back," said Ben.
2. "You are clear to land," said the controller.
   "Thank you," replied the pilot.
3. "Why are you shouting?" asked dad.
   "You've shut my finger in the car door!" screamed mum.
4. "Halt!" said the watchman. "Who goes there?"
5. "You have won first prize," the judge said.
   "Thank you," said Mrs Button.

Page 11 (bottom)

"It's no good! I can't do my homework," said Josie.
"Why?" said her mother. "You always like doing maths."
"I just don't understand it. What am I going to do?" sobbed Josie.
"Let me see. Look! It's not page nine you should be doing, it's page eight.
No wonder you can't do it! You're looking at the wrong page," laughed
Josie's mother.

Page 12

"Come quickly, mum!" shouted Sarah.
"Whatever is the matter, dear?" asked her mother as she ran into the garden.
"Both the guinea pigs have escaped!" cried the little girl.
"How on earth did that happen?" said mum. "We are always so careful to
shut the door of the hutch."
"It's my fault," sobbed Sarah, "because I didn't close it properly."
"Don't waste time crying!" exclaimed her mother. "Let's look for them!"
They searched the vegetable garden and the flower beds and the field where their
old donkey grazed, but all in vain.
Sarah was very unhappy. "I shall never see my lovely guinea pigs again," she wept.
At school next day she kept saying to herself, "Why was I so careless? Why didn't I
shut the door properly?"
She need not have worried. When she came home from school, her mother
greeted her with a big smile.
"I've just found the guinea pigs!" she said. "They are hiding in the old fox hole at the
end of the field. Dad is coming home this minute to help catch them," she added.
"Thank goodness!" shrieked Sarah. "What a relief!
The guinea pigs were soon back in their cosy hutch.
"I'll always look after them from now on," promised Sarah.

Page 13

1. The policeman said that I must not park there. 2. The little boy said that he had seen that video. 3. The window cleaner said that those windows were very dirty. 4. The paperboy said that he thought that dog would bite him. 5. The climbing instructor said that he/she hoped that she would reach the summit.

Page 14 (top)

1. The little girl shouted, "I can swim forty lengths." 2. The queen whispered, "My tiara is too big." 3. "It will snow tonight", the weather man warned. 4. "I have twisted my ankle," moaned Alice. 5. "There has been a hurricane in Florida," the journalist reported.

Page 14 (bottom)

1. "I have lost the book," admitted the teacher. 2. The check-out girl said that those eggs were broken. 3. "I do not like apples," declared Snow White. 4. The children agreed that they liked going to the Science Museum.

Page 15 (top)

1. Sleeping Beauty asked where she was. 2. The puzzled detective enquired why the door was unlocked. 3. I asked the surveyor if he could see the water in the well. 4. The astronomer asked the children how many stars they could see.

Page 15 (bottom)

1. I asked the photographer, "When will the proofs be ready?" 2. Sherlock Holmes asked Doctor Watson, "Do you want to study the case?" 3. The chef asked, "When will the potatoes be ready?" 4. The bus driver asked, "Do you want to get off at the next stop?"

Answer page (cont.)

Page 16 (top)
1. When I go camping I need all these things: a sleeping bag, a torch, a pan and some matches. 2. I like bright colours: red, orange, yellow and green. 3. Mrs Blob bought lots of fruit: apples, pears and bananas. 4. I like everything about the seaside: the sea, the sand and the candyfloss. 5. My new mountain bicycle has everything: wide wheels, twenty five gears and a racing saddle.

Page 16 (bottom)
1. The postman delivers mail six days a week: Monday, Tuesday, Wednesday, Thursday, Friday, Saturday. 2. Watch the traffic lights change: green to amber to red. 3. The colours of the rainbow are in this order: red, orange, yellow, green, blue, indigo, violet. 4. Put the seasons of the year into the right order: spring, summer, autumn, winter.

Page 17 - (bottom)
1. We cannot ski: it is raining and there is no snow. 2. I went to the library: I wanted a science book. 3. The dog was frightened: the firework had made a loud bang. 4. We need to use suntan lotion: the sun is very hot today. 5. We had to stand: the train was very full. 6. Don't ice the cake: the icing is too soft.

Page 18 (bottom)
1. Do not worry: every cloud has a silver lining. 2. Juliet asked: "O Romeo, Romeo! Wherefore art thou Romeo?" 3. My dad arrived late: better late than never. 4. Martin Luther King once said: "I have a dream." 5. Do it now; a stitch in time saves nine. 6. Winston Churchill said: "I have nothing to offer but blood, toil, sweat and tears."

Page 19 (bottom)
1. The baby was crying; she was unhappy in her cot. 2. The ring sparkled; the diamonds flashed. 3. No man is an island; everyone needs a friend. 4. We have to go; the taxi is waiting. 5. A wise man is often silent; a fool often talks too much. 6. It was a clear, cloudless night; the stars shone brightly.

Page 20 (top)
1. The old lady was shivering; her coat was too thin. 2. He began the book; he didn't finish it. 3. I am going to see my friend; I will take her Christmas present with me. 4. I do not trust him; he lied to me. 5. He has left already; I will not see him.

Page 20 (bottom)
1. My dog is fat because he eats too much. 2. The iron was too hot so I ruined my skirt. 3. I went to the library and I used the reference books. 4. He sent her a message but she cannot meet him. 5. It was difficult to read since one of the light bulbs was missing.

Page 22
The three children love the large old house with its two staircases. There are five bedrooms. This means that Katy and her sisters can each have their own bedroom.

Outside there are two barns; the small one has been made into a den for the girls. On a wet day they and their friends can play music as loudly as they like without disturbing anyone.

Now the girls live in the country they are a long way from their school. The school bus stops outside the farmhouse. They enjoy the journey with their friends.